SUPER-VILLAINS

LONDON, NEW YORK, MUNICH,
MELBOURNE AND DELHI

Senior Editor Victoria Taylor
Designer Sandra Perry
Senior Designer Anna Formanek
Design Manager Nathan Martin
Managing Editor Laura Gilbert
Publishing Manager Julie Ferris
Publishing Director Simon Beecroft
Pre-production Producer Rebecca Fallowfield
Producer Melanie Mikellides
Jacket Designer Jon Hall

First published in Great Britain in 2013
by Dorling Kindersley Limited
80 Strand, London, WC2R 0RL

13 14 15 16 17 10 9 8 7 6 5

Page design copyright © 2013 Dorling Kindersley Limited

LEGO, the LEGO logo, the Brick and Knob configurations
and the Minifigure are trademarks of the LEGO Group.
© 2013 The LEGO Group

Produced by Dorling Kindersley under licence from
the LEGO Group

A catalogue record for this book is available
from the British Library.

ISBN: 978-1-40936-612-6

Colour reproduction by Media Development and Printing, UK
Printed and bound in China by L.Rex

Discover more at
www.dk.com
www.LEGO.com

Contents

SUPER-VILLAINS

Written by Victoria Taylor

Batman   Robin

The Heroes

The world's super heroes have got a lot of work to do.
They must keep the crime-filled streets of Gotham City and Metropolis safe.

There is a frightening group of super-villains causing havoc! They enjoy making things as difficult as possible for the super heroes.

Wonder Woman

Superman

Gotham City

Gotham City is a dark and dangerous place. There is so much crime there that the city's police need help from super heroes to keep it safe.

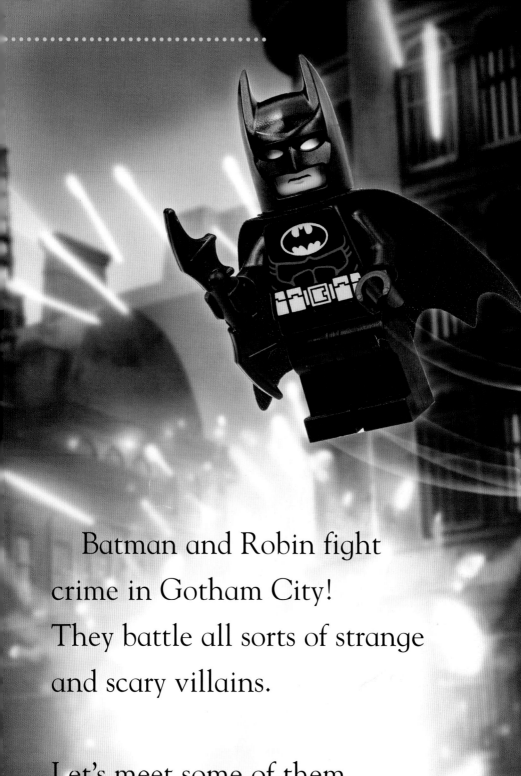

Batman and Robin fight
crime in Gotham City!
They battle all sorts of strange
and scary villains.

Let's meet some of them . . .

The Joker

The Joker is one villain that Batman does not find funny! He has a white face, bright green hair and a permanent smile.

The Joker does not take being bad too seriously. He has all kinds of joke-themed weapons and gadgets.

He loves to surprise Batman whenever he can. Bang!

Mr Freeze

Mr Freeze enjoys doing battle on ice!

He likes cold, snowy conditions that match his frosty personality.

He can turn his enemies into
blocks of ice with a freeze pistol
that freezes them on the spot.

Luckily, Batman is too
fast for him!

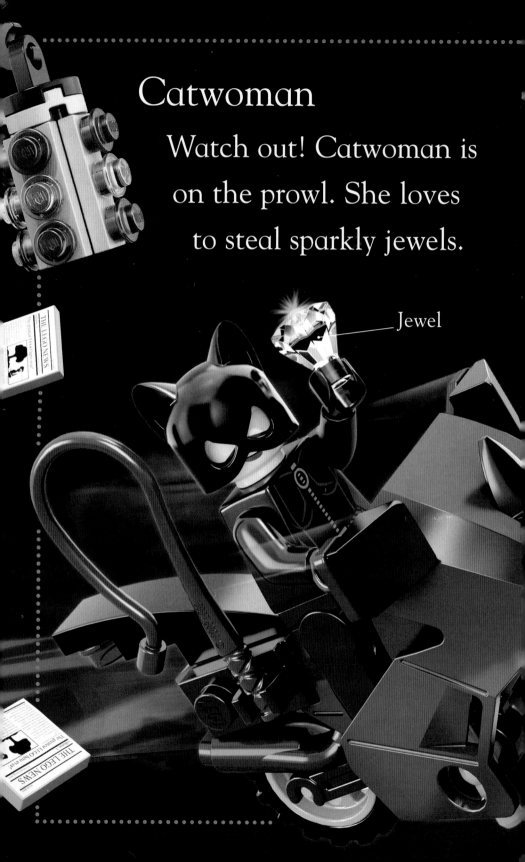

Catwoman

Watch out! Catwoman is on the prowl. She loves to steal sparkly jewels.

Jewel

Catwoman can climb tall
buildings with ease. She wears
a black suit that helps her hide
from Batman and blend into
the night.

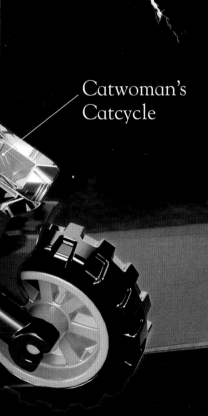

Catwoman's
Catcycle

Well-protected
Catwoman carries a
whip and wears a mask
to hide her identity
when stealing jewels.

Harley Quinn

Harley Quinn used to be
a doctor at Arkham Asylum.
She once treated the Joker there.

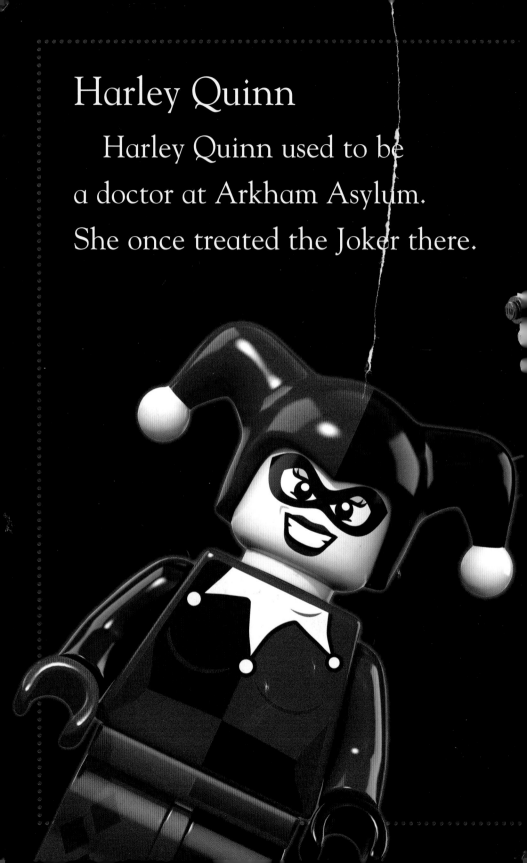

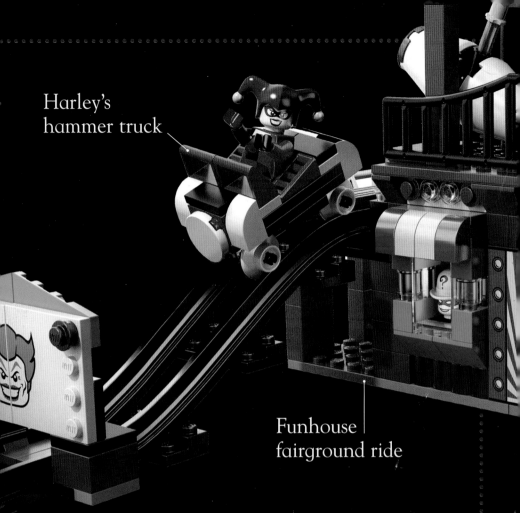

Harley's hammer truck

Funhouse fairground ride

But Harley ended up forming a criminal duo with the Joker instead of curing him of his madness! The two villains are on a joint mission to defeat Batman once and for all.

Two-Face

Two-Face is double trouble.
He was in an accident that
turned him into the terrifying
villain Two-Face.
He is a master bank robber.

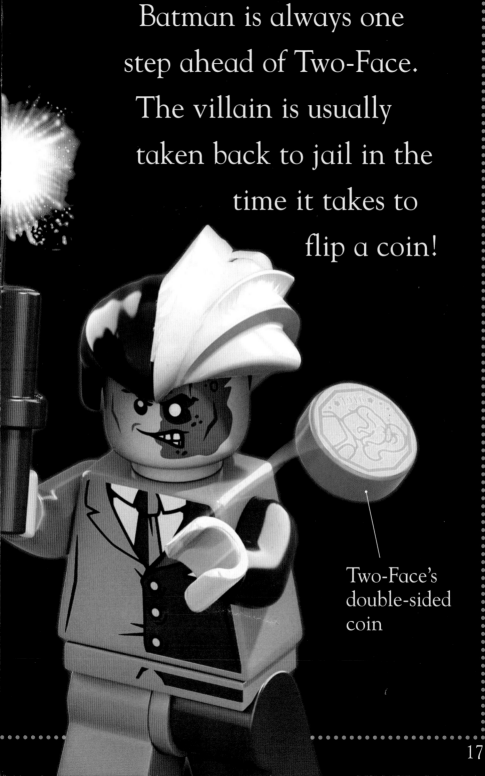

Batman is always one step ahead of Two-Face. The villain is usually taken back to jail in the time it takes to flip a coin!

Two-Face's double-sided coin

Scarecrow

Scarecrow looks terrifying with his glowing red eyes. He wears ragged clothes and loves to scare people.

He flies an old-fashioned biplane, which has four wings.

He might look horrific, but Batman isn't scared of him!

Bane's Tumbler

Bane

Bane is one of the Batman's toughest enemies. He is very strong. He is also very clever and is good at planning his crimes in great detail.

Bane wears a frightening
mask and drives an
armoured Tumbler vehicle.

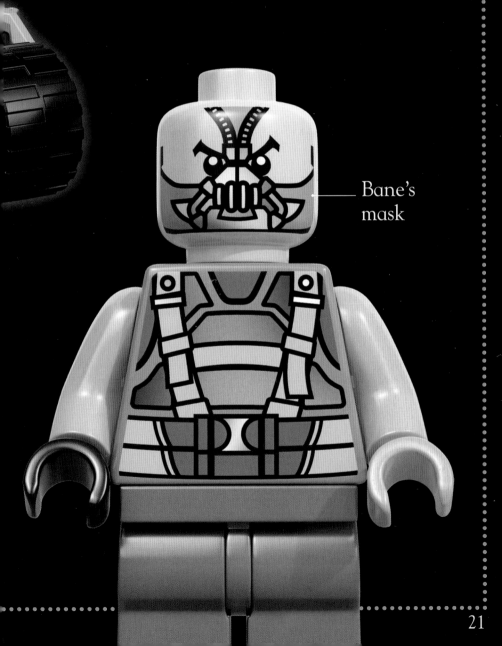

Bane's
mask

The Riddler

Can you guess who this is?
It's the Riddler! He loves puzzles
and word games.
He even carries
a cane in the
shape of a
question mark!

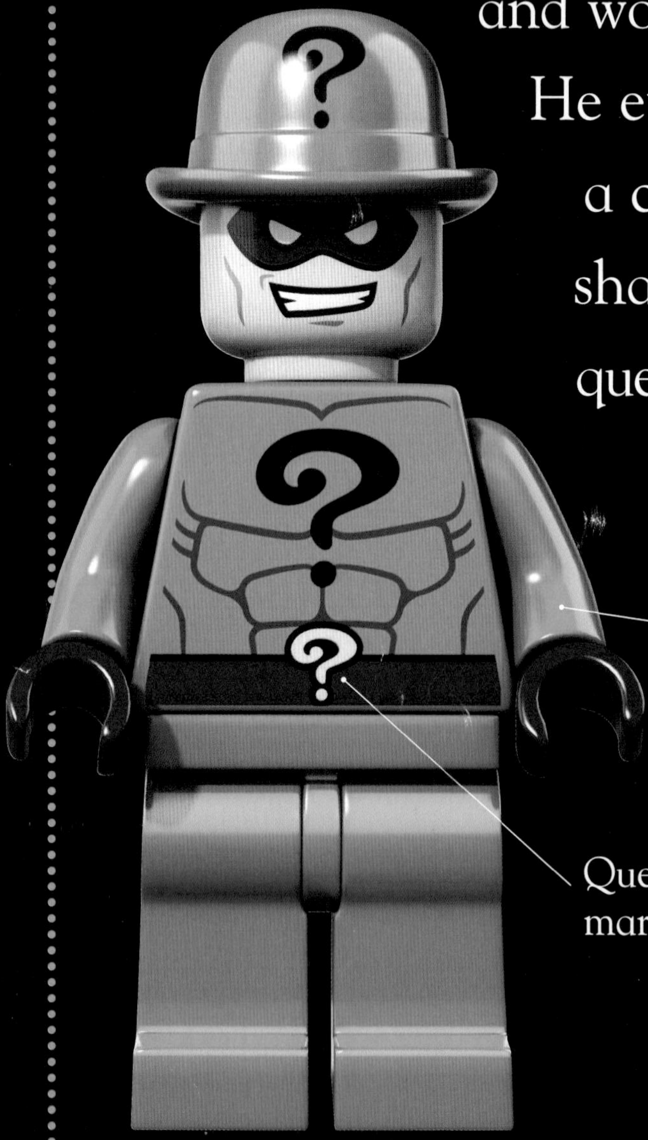

Green suit

Question
mark belt

The Riddler always leaves
lots of clues about his crimes.
He loves watching Batman
struggle to solve his puzzles
and riddles.

Poison Ivy

Poison Ivy is one
of Batman's most
dangerous foes.
She has always
liked plants more
than people.
Poison Ivy uses
plant toxins to control the
minds of others. She wears
a costume made of leaves.

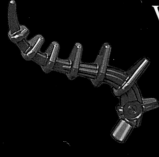

Vine
Poison Ivy has a whip
made from a vine.
She wants Gotham
City to become overrun
with wicked weeds.

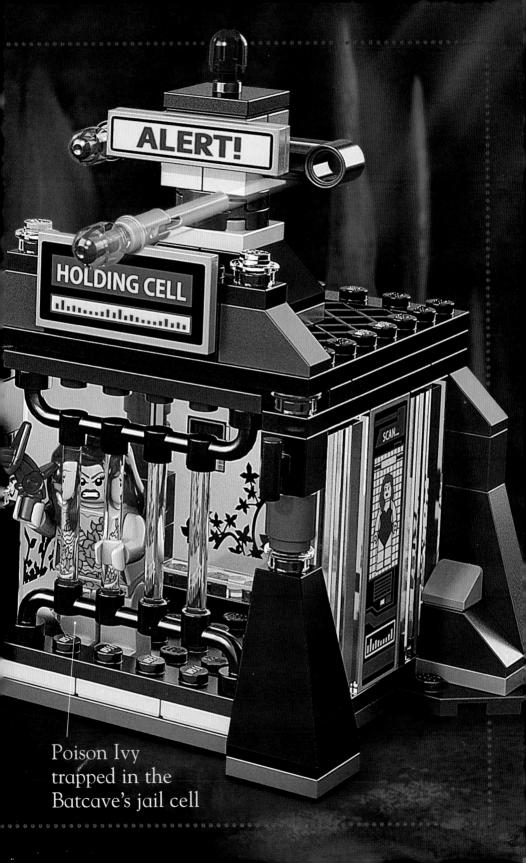

ALERT!

HOLDING CELL

SCAN...

Poison Ivy
trapped in the
Batcave's jail cell

Metropolis

Batman and Robin have got Gotham City covered. Metropolis also has super hero protection against criminals and villains – Superman!

Wonder Woman arrives in
Metropolis to help
Superman.
Together they
tackle the city's
most deadly
super-villain,
Lex Luthor . . .

Lex Luthor

Lex Luthor has been
Superman's enemy
for a long time.
Bald baddie Lex
is a rich
businessman
and inventor.

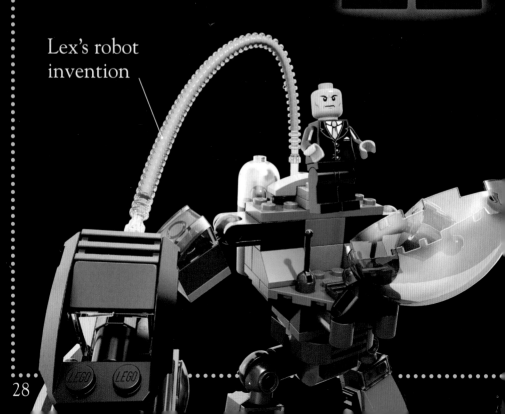

Lex's robot
invention

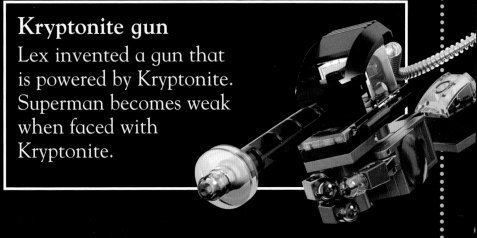

Kryptonite gun
Lex invented a gun that is powered by Kryptonite. Superman becomes weak when faced with Kryptonite.

Lex loves to create his own weapons and equipment to help him to defeat Superman.

He has even invented a big robot that he can sit inside and control. It is super-strong but it is no match for Superman and Wonder Woman. He will have to invent something else!

Locked Up

The planet's super-villains have many different powers and tricks up their sleeves. However, in the end they are no match for the super heroes!

The villains end up behind bars for their crimes.

Well done, super heroes!

Quiz

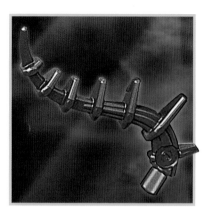

1. Whose weapon is this?

2. What is Catwoman's vehicle called?

3. What is this villain called?

4. Whose biplane is this?

Answers: 1. Poison Ivy's **2.** The Catcycle **3.** Harley Quinn **4.** Scarecrow's